Try Not to Laugh Challenge

WOULD YOU RATHER?

CAMPFIRE
EDITION

A CAMPING-THEMED INTERACTIVE & FAMILY FRIENDLY QUESTION GAME
FOR BOYS, GIRLS, KIDS TWEENS & TEENS

Howling Moon Books

WELCOME TO THE

Try Not to Laugh Challenge ™

WOULD YOU RATHER?

Camping Edition

Plus
Two Bonus Camping Games!

WHiCH iS WORSE?

AND

THiS OR THAT?

Try Not to Laugh Challenge ™

WOULD YOU RATHER?

Camping Edition

Rules:

Pick your team, or go one on one.

Each team will take turns reading the "Would you Rather" questions out loud.

The oldest player gets to go first.

Team 1 will read the "Would you Rather" question and choose an answer.

Team 1 will then explain in the funniest way why they chose that answer.

If Team 2 laughs, Team 1 gets a point!

Players must always pick one of the choices, but they can also add silly ideas of their own to their "Would you Rather" choice!

The Team that ends up with the most points, WINS!

TIP:

You can make silly faces, funny sound effects, use goofy voices, wacky movements or anything laughable when reading your choices!

BONUS TIP:

Teams can keep track of their own score, or a score keeper can be chosen for the game.

WOULD YOU RATHER?

Would you Rather...learn that the campers next to you are aliens
OR
Learn that the campers next to you are shape-shifters?

Would you Rather...roast a giant slug over a campfire
OR
Roast a giant spider over a campfire?

Would you Rather...play Sardines
OR
Hide and Seek?

WOULD YOU RATHER?

Would you Rather...go caving
OR
Go rock climbing?

Would you Rather...share a tent
with a snapping turtle
OR
Share a tent with a skunk?

Would you Rather...lose your hiking
poles
OR
Lose your water bottle?

WOULD YOU RATHER?

Would you Rather...have a pack of
hungry wolves circling your tent
OR
Have a pair of vultures perched
on top of your tent?

Would you Rather...play Bingo with
a cheater
OR
Play Hangman with a bad speller?

Would you Rather...run into Bigfoot
in the woods
OR
See a UFO flying overhead?

WOULD YOU RATHER?

Would you Rather...get bitten by
a raccoon
OR
Get bitten by a snake?

Would you Rather...trip and fall
face-first on an underground nest
of angry ground bees
OR
Back into a giant cactus?

Would you Rather...try to whittle a
walking stick that is full of fire ants
OR
Make leaf jewelry out of poison
sumac leaves?

WOULD YOU RATHER?

Would you Rather...have to start every conversation with, "Sup fam?"
OR
Have to start every conversation with, "Howdy partner?"

Would you Rather...have to end every conversation with, "I'm gonna dip!"
OR
Have to end every conversation with, "Don't leave me on read."

Would you Rather...play Corn Hole
OR
Play Blongo?

WOULD you RATHER?

Would you Rather...pitch a tent
during a hurricane
OR
Pitch a tent in a hailstorm?

Would you Rather...play pranks on
your camping trip
OR
Tell hilarious jokes on your
camping trips?

Would you Rather...camp with
someone who hates camping
OR
Camp with someone who is a
daredevil?

WOULD you RATHER?

Would you Rather...forget the
tent stakes
OR
Forget the hammer?

Would you Rather...have a leaky
canteen in the middle of the desert
OR
Be in a leaky canoe in the middle
of a huge lake?

Would you Rather...have a
pizza-making machine in your cabin
OR
Have an ice cream machine in your
cabin?

WOULD you RATHER?

Would you Rather...go over Niagara
Falls in a barrel
OR
Walk a tightrope over the Grand
Canyon?

Would you Rather...play
camping-themed Madlibs
OR
Have a campsite scavenger hunt?

Would you Rather...run faster
than a mountain lion
OR
Fly higher than an eagle?

WOULD YOU RATHER?

Would you Rather...always talk in rhymes
OR
Always talk like Yoda?

Would you Rather...camp in all of America's National Parks
OR
Be able to camp at the Seven Wonders of the World?

Would you Rather...go birdwatching
OR
Go fishing?

WOULD YOU RATHER?

Would you Rather...go camping
with a witch
OR
Go camping with a werewolf?

Would you Rather...go glamping
OR
Become a survivalist?

Would you Rather...sketch wildlife
OR
Sketch a landscape?

WOULD you RATHER?

Would you Rather...use GPS that
has glitches
OR
Use a paper map?

Would you Rather...forget your
backup batteries
OR
Forget your firestarter?

Would you Rather...wake up to
the smell of pancakes
OR
Wake up to the smell of bacon?

WOULD YOU RATHER?

Would you Rather...have a pet
hedgehog
OR
A pet tree frog?

Would you Rather...cook in
foil packs
OR
Cook in a dutch oven?

Would you Rather...burp after
you ask a question
OR
Fart after you answer a question?

WOULD you RATHER?

Would you Rather...have
camaflouge-colored hair
OR
rainbow-colored hair?

Would you Rather...communicate
by using selfies
OR
Communicate by using emojis?

Would you Rather...go kayaking
OR
go canoeing?

Would you Rather...have flies
buzzing around your head
OR
Mosquitoes biting your ankles?

WOULD you RATHER?

Would you Rather...have a new
National Park named after you
OR
Have a new camping tool named
after you?

Would you Rather...hike into woods
that are inhabited by dragons
OR
Hike into woods that are
inhabited by unicorns?

Would you Rather...talk like
Scooby-Doo
OR
Talk like Mickey Mouse?

WOULD YOU RATHER?

Would you Rather...have a shadow
hand puppet show at night
OR
Play glow stick ring toss at night?

Would you Rather...have to dance
around the campfire to light it
OR
Have to sing a song to the firewood
before you light it?

Would you Rather...play Two Truths
and a Lie
OR
Never have I ever?

WOULD YOU RATHER?

Would you Rather...start a blog
about camping in the snow
OR
Start a blog about camping in
the desert?

Would you Rather...be followed by
real pokemon
OR
Be followed by ghosts?

Would you Rather...drop your phone
in the outhouse toilet
OR
drop your phone in the lake?

WOULD YOU RATHER?

Would you Rather...get stuck in a
giant spider web
OR
Get lost in an underground cave?

Would you Rather...be able to
identify poison berries
OR
Be able to identify poison
mushrooms?

Would you Rather...camp inside a
video game
OR
Camp inside your favorite show?

WOULD YOU RATHER?

Would you Rather...have teeth like
a beaver
OR
Have horns like a pronghorn
antelope?

Would you Rather...go to summer
camp for the whole summer
OR
Go to summer camp for
two weeks?

Would you Rather...go fishing in
a lake
OR
Go fly fishing?

WOULD YOU RATHER?

Would you Rather...go for a year
without the internet
OR
Go for a year without music?

Would you Rather...be in a cave
full of bats
OR
Be in a swamp full of alligators?

Would you Rather...catch frogs
for fun
OR
Catch lightning bugs for fun?

WOULD you RATHER?

Would you Rather...have no clean
clothes for a week
OR
Have no dry clothes for a week?

Would you Rather...find fresh
gnome footprints
OR
Find fresh leprechaun footprints?

Would you Rather...eat a
toasted marshmallow that fell
in the dirt
OR
Eat a burnt marshmallow?

WOULD YOU RATHER?

Would you Rather...have a jacuzzi
in your cabin
OR
Have a theater in your cabin?

Would you Rather...brush your
teeth with sunscreen
OR
Take a shower with bug repellant?

Would you Rather...camp in a
treehouse that is 100 feet
in the air
OR
Camp in a shelter that is 100
feet underground?

WOULD YOU RATHER?

Would you Rather...run a YouTube channel teaching outdoor survival skills
OR
Run a blog on outdoor survival tips?

Would you Rather...pack extra hot chocolate
OR
pack extra popcorn?

Would you Rather...swing off a rope into a lake
OR
Dive off a floating dock?

WOULD YOU RATHER?

Would you Rather...be invisible
OR
Be able to change your appearance
at will?

Would you Rather...find a bunch
of earwigs in your sleeping bag
OR
Find a family of slugs in your
sleeping bag?

Would you Rather...eat a plate of
raw fish
OR
Eat a bag of soggy bread?

WOULD you RATHER?

Would you Rather...do a backflip
over the campfire
OR
Do a handstand over poison ivy?

Would you Rather...take selfies
with cute forest animals
OR
Take selfies with scary bugs?

Would you Rather...be a famous
forest ranger
OR
Be a famous geologist?

WOULD YOU RATHER?

Would you Rather...fillet a fish
OR
Skin a frog?

Would you Rather...start a rock
collection
OR
Start a bug collection?

Would you Rather...sleepwalk
every night on your camping trip
OR
Talk in your sleep every night
on your camping trip?

WOULD you RATHER?

Would you Rather...be able to
communicate with plants
OR
Be able to communicate with
animals?

Would you Rather...be on a camping
trip during a zombie apocalypse
OR
Be on a camping trip during a
worldwide meteor shower?

Would you Rather...live in a world
that is run by animals
OR
Live in a world that is run by
insects?

WOULD YOU RATHER?

Would you Rather...see the Loch Ness monster emerge from a lake
OR
See the swamp creature emerge from a swamp?

Would you Rather...grow a beaver tail
OR
Grow moose antlers?

Would you Rather...go to the bathroom in a cathole
OR
Go to the bathroom in an outhouse?

WOULD YOU RATHER?

Would you Rather...be in the boat
all day
OR
Hike the trails all day?

Would you Rather...play Ghost in
the Graveyard
OR
Capture the Flag?

Would you Rather...camp in the
winter
OR
Camp in the summer?

WOULD you RATHER?

Would you Rather...go rock climbing
with Spiderman
OR
Go skydiving with Superman?

Would you Rather...have a
photographic memory
OR
Be able to speed read?

Would you Rather...backpack
only at night
OR
Backpack only in the rain?

WOULD YOU RATHER?

Would you Rather...set up camp
next to an active volcano
OR
Set up camp on a mountain known
for landslides?

Would you Rather...have a thumb
wrestling tournament
OR
Play hiking stick limbo?

Would you Rather...have an
endless supply of mountain pies
on your camping trip
OR
Have an endless supply of s'mores
on your camping trip?

WOULD YOU RATHER?

Would you Rather...be in charge of cooking on your camping trip
OR
Be in charge of washing dishes on your camping trip?

Would you Rather...release sky lanterns
OR
Shoot off fireworks?

Would you Rather...Go backcountry camping
OR
Camp at a campground?

WOULD you RATHER?

Would you Rather...play card games
OR
Play cherades?

Would you Rather...be in a slingshot contest
OR
Be in a axe throwing contest?

Would you Rather...cook Jiffy Pop over the campfire
OR
Cook a dump cake over the campfire?

WOULD YOU RATHER?

Would you Rather...catch a fish
with a 2-liter bottle fish trap
OR
Catch a fish with your hands?

Would you Rather...have to sleep
in a haunted cabin on your
camping trip
OR
Eat only sardines and hot peppers
on your camping trip?

Would you Rather...camp in a
trailer tent
OR
Camp in an RV?

WOULD YOU RATHER?

Would you Rather...go river tubing
OR
Go water skiing?

Would you Rather...have your backpack smell like rotten fish
OR
Have your backpack smell like bear poop?

Would you Rather...tell ghost stories around the campfire
OR
Play guitar and sing songs around the campfire?

WOULD YOU RATHER?

Would you Rather...bring your best
friend on your camping trip
OR
Bring your dog on your camping
trip?

Would you Rather...sleep in a cabin
full of mosquitoes
OR
Sleep in a cabin full of no-see-ums?

Would you Rather...skip stones
on a lake
OR
Build a sandcastle on the beach?

WOULD YOU RATHER?

Would you Rather...eat moldy bread
OR
Eat rotten fruit?

Would you Rather...lounge around
the campsite
OR
Rappel down a cliff?

Would you Rather...be able to tie
perfect knots
OR
Be able to build a survival shelter?

WOULD you RATHER?

Would you Rather...go Zorbing
OR
Go Paragliding?

Would you Rather...have a tail that
wags when you are happy
OR
Have ears that move back when
you are annoyed?

Would you Rather...use leaves for
toilet paper
OR
Use tree bark for toilet paper?

WOULD you RATHER?

Would you Rather...vacation in a hut
on the beach
OR
Vacation in an igloo on a glacier?

Would you Rather...wake up with
a mask like a raccoon
OR
Wake up with webbed feet like
a duck?

Would you Rather...be chased by
an angry moose
OR
Be chased by angry hornets?

WOULD YOU RATHER?

Would you Rather...travel into
the future
OR
Go back in time?

Would you Rather...ride on the
fastest roller coaster
OR
Go on the fastest bumper car
ride?

Would you Rather...meet George
Washington
OR
Meet today's President?

WOULD YOU RATHER?

Would you Rather...have a map if
you were lost in the woods
OR
have a compass if
you were lost in the woods?

Would you Rather...have wet feet
every morning
OR
Cold hands every night?

Would you Rather...wake up as
an cougar
OR
Wake up as an otter?

WOULD YOU RATHER?

Would you Rather...eat a dead
fish-flavored jelly bean
OR
Eat a diaper wipe-flavored jelly
bean?

Would you Rather...camp during an
alien invasion
OR
Camp during an invasion of dinosaurs
emerging from the center
of the earth?

Would you Rather...have an
animal tattoo
OR
Have a flower tattoo?

WOULD YOU RATHER?

Would you Rather...go on a zipline
down a mountain
OR
Bungee jump off of a high bridge?

Would you Rather...vacation in the
most remote location on earth
OR
Vacation in the most popular
campground in the world?

Would you Rather...be an owl
OR
Be a woodpecker?

WOULD YOU RATHER?

Would you Rather...travel back in time to watch how the pyramids were built
OR
Travel back in time see what the dinosaurs looked like?

Would you Rather...bushwack a new trail
OR
Go trail blazing?

Would you Rather...build a cabin out of Legos
OR
Build a virtual cabin using Minecraft?

WOULD YOU RATHER?

Would you Rather...go fishing
with Spongebob Squarepants
OR
Go hiking with Smokey the Bear?

Would you Rather...be an overnight
guest at the White House
OR
Be an overnight guest at
Buckingham Palace?

Would you Rather...start a feather
collection
OR
Start a seashell collection?

WOULD YOU RATHER?

Would you Rather...be able to camp anywhere in the world
OR
Be able to go glamping in a mansion-sized cabin?

Would you Rather...eat only hard-boiled eggs on your backpacking trip
OR
Eat only beef jerky on your backpacking trip?

Would you Rather...go camping with clean freaks
OR
Go camping with complete slobs?

WOULD YOU RATHER?

Would you Rather...plan to charge your phone with a solar panel on your trip
OR
Plan to charge your phone with water power on your trip?

Would you Rather...have an eel in your backpack
OR
Grubs in your shirt?

Would you Rather...camp near a waterfall
OR
Camp near a lake?

WOULD YOU RATHER?

Would you Rather...be allergic to fresh air
OR
Be allergic to the sun?

Would you Rather...be a vulture
OR
A hawk?

Would you Rather...camp in a winnebago
OR
Go overlanding?

WOULD YOU RATHER?

Would you Rather...forget to pack
the bug repellant
OR
Forget to pack the sunscreen?

Would you Rather...swim with
a mermaid
OR
Ride a unicorn?

Would you Rather...be attacked
by a porcupine
OR
Be sprayed by a skunk?

WOULD you RATHER?

Would you Rather...camp in outer space
OR
Camp on the bottom of the ocean?

Would you Rather...be chased by a swarm of bees
OR
Be chased by a pack of wolves?

Would you Rather...have the power to control fire
OR
Have the power to control the weather?

WOULD YOU RATHER?

Would you Rather...go for a
midnight swim
OR
Go for a nighttime walk?

Would you Rather...camp in a yurt
OR
Camp in a cabin?

Would you Rather...camp near
a cave
OR
Camp near a geyser?

WOULD you RATHER?

Would you Rather...go windsurfing
OR
Go snowboarding?

Would you Rather...bring back an
extinct species
OR
Discover a new species in the
forest?

Would you Rather...eat grubs for
a snack
OR
Eat grasshoppers for a snack?

WOULD YOU RATHER?

Would you Rather...be able to
identify animal tracks
OR
Be able to identify animal scat?

Would you Rather...be able to spot
animal homes and hiding places
OR
Be able to identify animal's feeding
habits in the wild?

Would you Rather...forget to pack
the first-aid kit
OR
Forget to pack the toilet paper?

Try Not to Laugh Challenge ™
THiS OR THAT?
Camping Edition

Rules:
The player with the next birthday gets to go first.

S'mores are not just a campfire treat anymore! Crazy new s'mores are now a year-round goodie! Players will take turns reading the "This or That" question out loud and pick their favorite ooey-gooey s'more!

The Reader will then explain in the funniest way why they chose that answer.

If any player laughs, the Reader gets a point!

Players must always pick one of the choices, but they can also add some silly ideas of their own to their "This or That" choice!

The Player that ends up with the most points, WINS!

BONUS TIP:
Add some fun to this game? Hand out 20 mini marshmallows or 20 bite sized s'more-flavored treats to each player. Players will eat a treat when they get a point. First player with no treats, WINS!

THIS OR THAT?

S'mores Monkey Bread Muffins
OR
Cresent Rolls S'mores?

Pear, Brie, and Dark Chocolate
S'mores
OR
Cayenne Pepper S'mores?

Popcorn S'mores
OR
Chocolate Chip Cookie Nutella
S'mores?

THiS OR THAT?

Banana Split S'mores
OR
Ice Cream Sandwich S'mores?

Peanut Butter Cookie S'mores
OR
Cookies & Cream White Chocolate
S'mores?

Caramel Green Apple S'mores
OR
Milkshake S'mores?

THiS OR THAT?

Campfire S'more Bread Pudding
OR
S'mores Creme Brulee?

Grilled Cheese S'mores
OR
Cheese Ball S'mores?

Fudge S'mores
OR
Waffle S'mores?

THiS OR THAT?

Strawberry Shortcake S'mores
OR
Chocolate Covered Strawberry
S'mores?

Dark Chocolate Brownie S'mores
OR
Teddy Graham S'mores mix?

Reece's S'mores
OR
S'mores Pops?

THIS OR THAT?

Brown Sugar Bacon S'mores
OR
Cheesecake Bars S'mores?

Rice Krispies Treat S'mores
OR
Berries and Cream S'mores?

Peeps S'mores
OR
Chocolate Kiss S'mores?

THIS OR THAT?

Gingerbread Cookie S'mores
OR
Peppermint Bark S'mores?

Hot Chocolate S'mores
OR
S'mores Fondue?

Macaron S'mores
OR
Caramel Churro S'mores?

THIS OR THAT?

Peanut Butter Banana S'mores
OR
Chocolate Covered Pretzel S'mores?

S'moreos
OR
Snickers S'mores?

Milky Way S'mores
OR
Kit Kat S'mores?

THiS OR THAT?

Chocolate Covered Potato Chip
S'mores
OR
Fudge Striped Cookie S'mores?

Peppermint Patty S'mores
OR
Toasted Coconut S'mores?

Trail Mix S'mores
OR
Granola S'mores?

THIS OR THAT?

Ice Cream Sundae S'mores
OR
Peanut Butter & Jelly S'mores?

S'mores Stuffed French Toast
OR
Breakfast Oatmeal S'mores?

Rainbow Sprinkles S'mores
OR
Grilled Pineapple S'mores?

THiS OR THAT?

Coffee Cake S'mores
OR
Pancake S'mores?

Taco S'mores
OR
Quesadilla S'mores?

Lemon Meringue Pie S'mores
OR
Orange Marmalade S'mores?

Fluffernutter S'mores
OR
Burnt Marshmallow S'mores?

Try Not to Laugh Challenge ™

WHiCH iS WORSE?

Camping Edition

Rules:

The player who will be celebrating their birthday next gets to be the first Reader.

Make sure to read the phrase "Which is Worse?" at the beginning of each question.

The Reader will read the question and have everyone say their answer out loud.
(Players will take turns reading the "Which is Worse" choices.)

The player/players that pick the LEAST popular choice will get 1 point.

Allow the player/players to explain in the funniest way possible why they chose the LEAST popular choice!

The player/players that end up with 10 points, WINS!

BONUS TIP:
Players can keep track of their own score, or a score keeper can be picked for all the players.

WHICH IS WORSE?

Finding maggots in your food
OR
Losing control of the campfire?

Setting up camp in the dark
OR
Setting up camp in the rain?

Your new sleeping bag is too small
OR
Your new grill doesn't work?

WHiCH iS WORSE?

Sleeping in an overcrowded tent
OR
Sleeping in a leaky tent?

You forget to pack the mess kit
OR
You forget to pack the food?

Having poison ivy all over your
body
OR
Having blisters on the bottom
of both feet?

WHiCH iS WORSE?

Sleeping on tree roots under your tent
OR
Sleeping on a big rock under your tent?

Tripping over the guy-line of the tent
OR
Stubbing your toe on the tent stake?

Loud neighbors at the campground
OR
Barking dogs at the campground?

WHICH IS WORSE?

Getting sick on your camping trip
OR
It rains every day on your
camping trip?

Getting lost in the woods during
the night
OR
You can hear a pack of animals
outside your tent?

The toilet paper gets wet
OR
You forget to pack the mosquito
spray?

WHICH IS WORSE?

The water filter breaks
OR
Your hiking boots fall apart?

Sleep in a tent that glows in the
dark (the bugs will come for miles)
OR
Sleep in a tent that is
bacon-scented? (uh-oh)

You forget to bring the back-up
tarps
OR
You forget to pack the suntan
lotion?

WHICH IS WORSE?

Creepy noises at night
OR
Can't find your flashlight?

You didn't pack enough clothes
for your trip
OR
You packed too many clothes
for your trip?

Strong winds blow all of your
camping equipment away
OR
An unexpected snowstorm?

WHiCH iS WORSE?

You forget to pack the tent
repair kit
OR
Forget to pack the overhead
lighting?

All of the campsites are booked
at the campground
OR
Getting lost?

Running face-first into a bee's nest
OR
Running face-first into a giant
spiderweb?

WHICH IS WORSE?

A rattlesnake sneaking into
your tent
OR
Scorpions creeping into
your tent?

Bringing your cat on your
camping trip
OR
Hiking in waders?

Playing Red Rover with a moose
OR
Playing Lawn Bowling with bighorn
sheep?

WHICH IS WORSE?

Mosquitoes
OR
Deer Flies?

Campfire smoke
OR
Sticky bug repellent?

Campers who play their radio
too loud
OR
Campers who play the bagpipes?

WHICH IS WORSE?

Being too cold at night
OR
Getting wet from the
morning dew?

You forgot to pack the hand
sanitizer
OR
You didn't pack enough toilet
paper?

Forgetting your first-aid kit
OR
You forget to pack your
repair kit?

WHiCH iS WORSE?

You are camping with someone
who will not stop talking
OR
You are camping with chronic
complainers?

A hot melted marshmallow drops
off the stick onto your bare leg
OR
You burn your tongue on a cup
of hot chocolate?

Losing your compass
OR
Your GPS starts to malfunction?

WHiCH iS WORSE?

You forgot to pack your rain gear
(and it's raining)
OR
You forgot to pack extra socks?

You are wearing perfume
(the bugs will love that!)
OR
Store your personal hygiene bag
in the tent?

Your sleeping bag smells very
musty
OR
Tent is covered with black mold?

WHICH IS WORSE?

Ten bee stings
OR
One hundred mosquito bites?

To be trapped in a well-used
outhouse for a day
OR
To be trapped in an RV bathroom
with a toilet that keeps backing
up for a day?

Have a fish face
OR
Have a fish body?

WHiCH iS WORSE?

Give up your phone for a month
OR
Give up your music for a month?

Ride the world's largest waterslide
OR
Ride the scariest roller-coaster?

Wake up before the sun rises
OR
Go to bed before the sun sets?

Leaches
OR
Ticks?

Be able to teleport yourself
anywhere in the world
OR
Be able to be invisible anytime
you want?

Bears
OR
Raccoons and rats?

Try Not to Laugh Challenge ™
WOULD YOU RATHER?
Camping Edition

If you enjoyed this book...

We would love it if you would leave us
a review on Amazon.com!
Just a few words about this book will
let others know what to expect.

Thank you bear-y much!

Howling Moon Books

Check out our

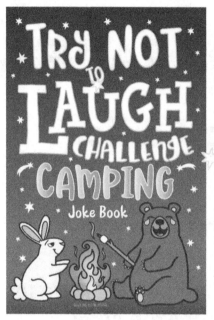

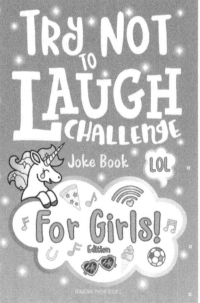

Howling Moon Books

other Joke Books!

Howling Moon Books

Check out our

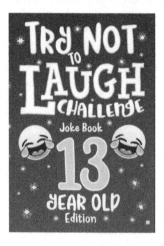

Howling Moon Books

other Joke Books!

Howling Moon Books

Made in the USA
Las Vegas, NV
23 June 2022